D0808316

Design is a Mind-Field

Cell-rejuvenating architecture & design

Rosalyn Dexter

Published by Outside the Bigger Box
www.outsidethebiggerbox.com

Text © Rosalyn Dexter 2015
Design & layout: Rosalyn Dexter

ISBN 978-0-9927836-1-7

Production: Blacker Limited
(www.blackerdesign.co.uk)

I want to thank the many people
who inspired and supported me
over the years, especially during
the writing of this book.
To name a few would be to
overlook the many.

I thank you all with appreciation
and much love.

Contents $\longrightarrow$

1.

Design in mind

Here in your hands is a small book that tells a big story, a story of cell regenerating, rejuvenating, life enhancing architecture and design.

Ever since the human experience began, man has sought ways to create shelter. Once we had satisfied our basic needs, our remit expanded and our preferences became more sophisticated. It did not occur to us that our developing aspirations around beauty and luxury, would offer us more than aesthetics and comfort. We certainly never imagined that the design of our environment could shape our life and have impact on our gene expression. Yet this is how our neural system is set up. We just haven't woven the strands of evidence together – until now.

Many forms of architecture have evolved over the eons. As we entered the 20th century, our skill in engineering and the development of new materials gave us a skyline of highrise buildings. An altitude supported by the invention of electricity, offering up light and elevators at the flick of a switch. The decades turned and as we headed towards the 21st century, in studying nature's design and the webs of spiders, we developed methods for integrating lightweight strength into our structures. We mimicked photosynthesis to produce solar powered energy, and created self-cleaning materials for our buildings by imitating the leaves of the lotus flower. As we furthered our knowledge of nature's processes, our potential for invention developed exponentially, adding an organic edge to our creativity.

Today we are exploring the brain like never before, and by unveiling its processes, we are at the dawn of a new frontier in design. The research into our cerebral workings is revealing how architecture and the design of our surroundings can interfere with the branches of our nervous system, rejuvenate our cells and alter our gene expression.

In synergy with how we function at the neurological level, our building functions more as a chrysalis for change than mere shelter.

Here is a big story distilled from the research of the finest minds in science. The resource material crosses psychology, neurobiology, neuroscience, genetics, cognitive linguistics, architecture and more. Woven together here in a very simple form, they reveal how the design of our environment has the ability to not only affect our cells, but even to shape our lives.

2.

Perceiving
the new

I have long been inspired by the ideas of the 20th century architect Richard Neutra. Celebrated for his American modernist style, he cared deeply about the psychological impact of buildings on the people they sheltered and had written volumes on the subject.

As far back as the 1940s he was suggesting we become more aware of how design can affect our psyche. A couple of decades later in the 1960s, evidence emerged on the influence of the environment at the psychological and neurological levels. Few took any particular notice. Then in 1979, there was a trial by Professor Ellen Langer at Harvard USA, which unveiled something that Neutra had not anticipated. Due to the way we function neurologically, our surrounding environment can, under certain circumstances, regenerate our cells and even trigger rejuvenation.

Professor Langer and her team had manipulated an environment for a group of geriatrics. The overall experience was set up to focus the participants' thoughts and feelings on their younger years. Memorabilia was used to induce and reinforce nostalgia in many forms. In the building itself, the decor, the attire worn by the staff and residents, the television programmes they watched, the radio programmes they listened to, and the bias of their conversations. All of these related to earlier decades, a time when the participants would have been 20 years younger.

By the end of just one week, the majority had experienced a reversal of visual thresholds and improvements in cognitive ability and IQ. Most had enhanced their manual dexterity and were moving with more pace, some were even discarding their walking sticks altogether. Surrounded by, and immersed in, a narrative of associations to their youth, within a period of a week their systems weren't just regenerating with cells replenishing and normalizing, they were renewing. Instead of a presumed atrophying of cells, they were rejuvenating.

This study remained in the shadows for nearly three decades, then in 2010 it was replicated in a BBC documentary. The results were phenomenal, again illustrating how our surroundings can not only regenerate, but also rejuvenate our cells. Millions of us watched on our TV screens, and yet it achieved very little attention from us or the press.

I was curious, not only with the evidence, but by our resistance to acknowledging it. I went in search of answers to the rejuvenating phenomenon as well as our reluctance to embrace it. A resistance that was highlighted in some studies by eminent neuroscientist Professor Erik Kandel. In his research into memory and learning, which won him the Nobel prize in 2005, Kandel revealed that new information needs to be repeatedly laid down to memory before we can digest it. Only through repetition and association, can information become familiar enough for us to eventually embrace it.

Aware of our resistance to the unfamiliar, I include evidence both old and new, across diverse fields of science. Some elements are repeated from different angles, this is to reinforce a familiarity with the concepts of cell-rejuvenating, regenerating, life enhancing architecture and design; so that they can become part of our daily life.

□ □

As the first few chapters unfold, we will be introduced to vision and our senses in general. We will look into the source of our imagination and inspiration, and how these weave with our daily reasoning. We unveil that real and imagined share similar neural pathways. We also learn how 'story' is fundamental to how we function at the neurological level, and this provides us with a framework for interpreting a design. We examine the influences of colour, shape and form, and how these, in conjunction with our imagination, enable our environment to trigger cellular change. We uncover science's revelations on consciousness, the particle field that underpins our atomic experience, and how time is subjective. Though these are outside the usual remit of design, here they illustrate the many varied ways in which we interact with our environment. As the book draws to a close, we reflect on epigenetics and how our environment affects our gene expression, our patterns of inheritance.

HOW I GOT HERE

A curiosity seeded in my youth brought me to this research. By the age of 13, I had lived in 30 homes on land and numerous cabins at sea. During this time, I attended over 24 schools around the globe, from which I gleaned an unusual perspective on life and habitat. The unconventional circumstances of this nomadic travelling, from one continent to another via boats, planes and automobiles, involved living in all manner of accommodation. The environment and how it nurtured, became an important focus for me.

When the peripatetic years drew to a close, it was time for university. I chose to study Art and Design. To pay for my studies I trained to be a dispensing optician, this was fortuitous as early on it fuelled an interest into how we see and the brain. This led me to study how we interpret what we see via our imagination, which in turn gave me a new perspective on aesthetics. I completed my studies with a thesis on architecture, and went on to develop a successful design company creating hybrid luxury lifestyle buildings.

It was over a decade ago that I became aware of exciting new evidence regarding the brain and environmental design. I decided to fund an extensive period of study into our psychological response to our environment. In researching the work of some of the finest minds of science, I connected up some of the clues that had captured my interest years before. This time, with access to new information, it altered my perspective on how design could serve us, at a profound level.

When explaining some of the complex elements of the research here, there is a benefit to my being a designer with an inner geek and a less than usual approach to learning. As a non-academic I present it in an accessible form.

Here design is offered as a fundamental product of our nature; for a future where strategic life-enhancing, cell-rejuvenating and regenerating design can become the norm.

Schopenhauer said

'All truth passes through three stages.

First, it is ridiculed.

Second, it is violently opposed.

Third, it is accepted as being

self-evident.'

3.

Perception

There have been many clues from eminent researchers over the years, on the influence of our environment. However, without the technology we have today to measure brain activity, they have often been overlooked. That said, a couple of decades before the trial at Harvard, scientists had uncovered the potential for our system to regenerate, though not to 'rejuvenate'. Frederick Gage and Peter Erickson were the first to uncover neurogenesis in the 1960s. They found that children could regenerate the tip of their finger, if a nerve was cut it eventually found pathways for regeneration.

At the time, the brain was still perceived as an atrophying machine. They did not know, as we do today, that our system has the continuing ability to normalise throughout adulthood, and that it is capable of restoration and rejuvenation to an earlier state – as illustrated by the participants in the Harvard study.

What has transpired is that, where previously our brain cells were thought to cease developing in adulthood, we now know they keep on developing. Our brain is neuroplastic. This means its cells are capable of renewing and reorganizing, increasing and decreasing in number in response to input. A process that continues until our demise.

Our brain is not hardwired as we had thought, it is soft-wired; experience changes it. However as it changes, this can either be towards regeneration or towards atrophy; the system is always switched on, and it can go either way.

A 1986 study by Professor Roger Ulrich of Pennsylvania University recorded an improved recovery rate for patients in a hospital ward with a window, compared to a ward without. There was an improved recovery rate of 20%, and a phenomenal 60% reduction in analgesic requirement. This accelerated improvement wasn't because bright sunshine was breaking through the window to an otherwise sterile ward [some windows in the study faced onto shaded light wells]. For some time the source of the accelerated recovery remained a mystery. As with the Harvard trial, by necessity the accrual of scientific data is at a slow burn – verifying detail takes time – but thanks to new technology, the evidence has arrived.

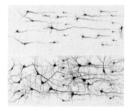

neurons firing together

Our nerve cells, our neurons, mostly operate by generating an electrical charge. This diffuses as electrochemical signals throughout our system. Change happens as neurons that fire-together wire-together, and those that fire-apart wire-apart, transforming our overall electrochemistry.

To help us grasp how we can influence change, let me first explain something of the mechanism of vision and the imagination.

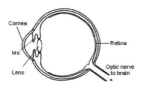

In each eye there are about 130 million photoreceptor cells. As these absorb light they send neural impulses via the optic nerve [which is basically an electrical cable] through our emotional centre, via at least one of our many integrated memory centres, and on into the reasoning and association areas of our brain. There an image is constructed from the light that was absorbed.

Alongside this, more than 30 regions of the brain fragment the images before us into a jigsaw of lines, horizontals, diagonals, curves, colours, shapes, textures, levels of brightness and more. Within 1/300th sec everything is deconstructed and reconstructed, having been imbued along the way with emotion and reasoning. In a blink.

DECONSTRUCTION
+ RECONSTRUCTION
+EMOTION + REASONING
X 1/300 SEC

= VISION

With a film reel we know that the images are spliced together frame-by-frame, so as to appear as a continuous stream; vision is similar. As our eyes survey our surroundings, we register the frames that are in 'our' focus and 'in' focus. We don't consciously register the sections between, our visual 'reel' moves so fast that we experience a continuous stream. This frame-by-frame 'leaping' of our focus is revealed when we look closely at someone's eyes as they look around a room, we will see their iris continually leaping, not moving in a smooth motion. As the iris moves from focal point to focal point, leaping past the sections in-between, via expectation, reasoned associations and more, our imagination fills in the micro-gaps. We fill them so fast that we perceive our version of our experience to simply be the way it is, we don't register that we have filled almost 2 hours out of every 24 in this way. The ease with which we fill in the gaps is illustrated by us siltl bineg albe to mkae a snese of this snetcene eevn thugoh it is selpt wnorg.

To the above we must add the impact of mood-alterers. In 2006 neuroscientists Irving Biederman and Edward Vessel were looking into aesthetics, when they unveiled some evidence that had been overlooked a quarter of a century before. It showed a high density of opioid receptors along the visual pathway. The visual pathway lies between the association cortex of our brain, interpreting what we see, and the mechanisms we harness for perspective. The opioid receptors scattered along this pathway, act as binding sites that trigger the release of mood-altering endorphins, such as serotonin and dopamine. Serotonin has been well documented as a mood-alterer – offering a feel-good factor. Dopamine has more recently been recognised as a molecule of addiction – inciting us to seek a chemical reward, giving us a charge like some experience with cocaine. So, as well as emotions and reasoning influencing what we perceive, and all that gap filling, we have mood-altering, pleasure-inducing substances affecting how we see what we see.

DECONSTRUCTION
+ RECONSTRUCTION + EMOTION
+ REASONING + IMAGINATION
+ GAP FILLING + MOOD ALTERERS
X 1/300 SEC

= PERCEPTION

What we 'perceive' is not necessarily what is literally out there, and what we each perceive is not the same. Our interpretation is fed by our personal feelings, reasoning and mood-altering, triggers. Alongside which, we have the influence of our personal history, culture and genetic predisposition.

As our cells renew and reorganise, the form of that change can be determined by the context and personal relevance of our surroundings. Those geriatrics in the Harvard study, rejuvenated in response to a youthful reminiscent environment, the surrounding narrative had that context and relevance for them.

I emphasise relevance and context here because we do not change arbitrarily. Our day-to-day life would be overwhelming if this were the case. Imagine the trauma for medical staff in an intensive care ward for example, it would be untenable. Our system has safety protocols, relevance and context are two of them.

DECONSTRUCTION
+ RECONSTRUCTION + EMOTION
+ REASONING + IMAGINATION
+ GAP FILLING + MOOD ALTERERS
+ HISTORY + GENETIC PREDISPOSITION
+ RELEVANCE +CONTEXT
+ NEUROPLASTICITY
X 1/300 SEC

= CELLULAR CHANGE

With regards to our susceptibility to change at the cellular level, neuroscientists have discovered that feelings are primary to reason. They found more neural connections running from our emotional centre to the neocortex [the part of the brain responsible for the evolution of our intelligence] than there are coming from our reasoning centre. Supporting what many of us have instinctively 'felt' – that feelings trump thoughts. The result is that we have a feeling-led influence, contributing to our 'reasoned' interpretation of what we 'imagine' we perceive. Maybe read 'that last' sentence again.

Where perception involves a feeling-led reasoning function, and mood altering triggers line the visual pathway, we are designed to weave our IMAGINATION into what we 'believe' we see. To some, integrating what we imagine we see into our interpretation of what we believe we see, may not sound all that outrageous, but the ramifications are!

With neuroplasticity, we know our cells are ever renewing and reorganising. If via interpretation, the input of information we respond to, is woven with what we imagine, then as our cells renew and reorganize, triggering change at the cellular level, that change is in response to what we IMAGINE.

Imagination was a contributing factor for the geriatrics on the Harvard trial. The surrounding narrative reflected youth and vitality, and this interwove with their imagination, encouraging rejuvenation as change.

DECONSTRUCTION
+ RECONSTRUCTION
+ FEELING- LED REASONING
+ IMAGINATION + GAP FILLING
+ MOOD ALTERERS + HISTORY
+ GENETIC PREDISPOSITION
+ RELEVANCE + CONTEXT
+ NEUROPLASTICITY
X 1/300 SEC

= CELL REJUVENATING,
REGENERATING
ARCHITECTURE AND DESIGN

4.

Wiring
the brain

I use the term 'narrative' when it comes to the meaning displayed in our surroundings. This is because pretty much everything emerges as a story, expressed neurologically as neurons firing their signals.

Today, we know more about our neural firings and the brain than ever before. We know which regions of the brain interpret buildings, which ones identify preferred locations, form, texture, contour, density, mass, colour, proportion and more. We can measure the influence and source of feelings, the impact of language and how symbols register.

With story being fundamental to how we function at the neurological level, note that we have identified many of the parts of our brain required for our environment to express a narrative. We have also identified the neural gateway for imagination, a necessary quality for story, it is the anterior superior temporal gyrus.

When it comes to story, researching psychiatrist Jeffrey Schwartz revealed evidence of what he calls self-directing neuroplasticity. He found that we have the ability to change the pathways of our own brain. We do this by interfering with and stimulating different thoughts. His early research was with sufferers of obsessive-compulsive disorder.

With this condition anxiety triggers repetitive behaviour, commonly known by the abbreviation OCD. Well known for his success in controlling this condition, Schwartz was invited to advise on the film Aviator. In this film Leo De Caprio was to play the lead role as Howard Hughes, the reclusive eccentric who famously suffered from OCD. Instead of guiding De Caprio to act like someone with the condition, Schwartz offered him some exercises so that he could train his brain to behave like someone 'with' OCD, thus interfering with his own neural branches. After filming, it took Di Caprio over a year to restore his neural wiring. Schwartz illustrated that not only can we rewire the pathways of our brain and direct the change, but the system goes both ways; just as we can train the brain to release OCD, we can train it to adopt its symptoms.

Our ability to rewire our brain by interfering with, and stimulating different thoughts, is relevant when approaching design as proposed here. Consider how the participants at Harvard were influenced by their environment. It reminded them of their younger years, in a way that stimulated their imagination, sufficiently to interfere with the growth of their neural branches. Their visual thresholds reversed, manual dexterity was enhanced and IQ improved – within one week. If we reflect on the earlier information on imagination, and consider Schwartz's work on growing different neural branches as we structure different thoughts, the role of the imagination and its influence on the growth of the branches of our neural system becomes more relevant.

In our suggestible, changeable system our imagination is at work on many levels. Reflected to some degree in the medical world confirming that optimists get sick proportionately less often than pessimists, and recover more speedily. We casually accept this, it has become familiar, but if we linger on what it suggests about our system, the implications are profound. An idea in ones mind can have a very real influence – at the cellular level.

5.

Story

I have emphasised that everything becomes a story, expressed as neural signals. To explain something of how we compose our story day-to-day, it helps to understand how our left and right brain communicate.

In a normally functioning brain the two hemispheres work together. The left hemisphere generally relates to the right side of the body and vice versa. Visual information that comes into the right eye is fed to the left hemisphere, and visual information coming into the left eye is fed to the right hemisphere. The left side of the brain generally deals with logic, language and mathematical computations, the right hemisphere with context and grasping the bigger picture. It is less reasoning and non verbal. The logical, verbal left side of the brain references sounds that form words and their syntax, the right side of the brain is more about the emotion within language. When it comes to speech, the right side deals with intonation. It is biased to creativity, spatial abilities and processing visual input; it makes an overall sense of what we experience. It is more active than the left when learning something new, whereas the left brain mostly deals with information as it becomes familiar. We communicate via a synergy of both sides of our brain.

Back in the 1950s, Nobel prize-winning neurobiologist Roger Sperry and his assistant, Michael Gazzaniga, were investigating patients whose connection between the left and right brain had been severed. They showed a picture of a snowy scene to the left eye of one of their subjects – for his right brain, and showed a chicken claw to his right eye – for his left brain. Then from a selection of images, they asked him to pick a relevant one with each hand.

With his right hand the subject chose a picture of a chicken – to match the claw directed to his left brain, and with the left hand he picked a picture of a snow shovel – responding to the snowy scene directed to his right brain. When asked why he chose them, he said that he had chosen the picture of a chicken because they had shown him the image of a chicken claw; that image had gone to his left logical verbal side.

When asked why he chose the snow shovel, in relation to the other image of a snowy scene that was directed to his less rea-soning non-verbal right brain, he said he didn't know. Then, he invented his own coherence and with conviction said, 'I chose the shovel because you need a shovel to clear out the chicken coup'. He invented a story that made a sense for him.

Story.

In a normal functioning brain, our left side offers up reasoning, while our right side gets creative, producing our unique experience. What the unveiling of neuroplasticity has enabled us to recognise, and the Harvard trial illustrated, is that over a period of time, in response to the surrounding environment and its narrative, we can change prescriptively at the cellular level.

DECONSTRUCTION + RECONSTRUCTION
+ FEELING- LED REASONING
+ IMAGINATION + GAP FILLING
+ MOOD ALTERERS
+ HISTORY + GENETIC PREDISPOSITION
+ RELEVANCE + CONTEXT
+ TEXTURE, COLOUR, DENSITY, MASS,
CONTOUR, PROPORTION, LANGUAGE,
SYMBOLS + LEFT AND RIGHT BRAIN
+ RELEVANCE + CONTEXT
X 1/300 SEC

= STORY + NEUROPLASTICITY

= LIFE-ENHANCING, CELL REJUVENATING,
REGENERATING ARCHITECTURE AND
DESIGN.

6.

Look
this way

In 1910 Richard Neutra was studying the work of the psychologist Wilhelm Wundt. Considered the father of modern psychology, Wundt had identified that both eye movement and head movement are inseparable; he found that the muscles around the eye are connected to the muscles of the head. This may not seem unexpected, except that decades later in 1976 at the Langley Porter Neuropsychiatric Institute in San Francisco, a study was done on the correlation of eye movements with neurophysiological processes. There they found that eye movements were related to specific cognitive processes. For the majority, eyes moving up and left triggered memory – like remembering the colour of one's room, whereas eyes moving up and right related to imagery and visual fantasy – such as imagining one's room painted a new colour. Eyes moving laterally left related to an auditory response when recalling our favourite tune – and so on.

Wundt identified that the movement of the eyes and head are inseparable and could affect neurological processes. The movement of our head can even affect our reference to linear time. A simple exercise illustrates this. If we raise our head to look upward, for most of us it is harder to think of the past than when looking down. Try it. By contrast when resting our head forward and looking down, most of us will find it harder to think of the future, compared to looking upward. Looking up allows for more visual constructs around imagination – it offers a more resourceful state for that. Whereas when looking down we tend to reflect inward and access feelings, fed by our inner dialogue and memories. Mind and body are connected in ways that we are not generally aware of or consider using to our advantage.

Where a manoeuvre of our head and line of sight can change our flow of thoughts with reference to a time line, we find not only is perception subjective, but so is time. Time being subjective in our general day to day should not surprise us. It is due to time's subjectivity that we can reflect on memories, to then have a downward glance enhance them.

Where the movement of the head can affect our thoughts, we find posture can effect our mood. If we lean forward and hang our head it is not only easier to think on the past, it is also harder to feel uplifted. Try it. If we hold our head and shoulders upright, it is harder to feel sad. Try that.

Many of us are familiar with seeing elderly people hunched over, looking at the ground in front of them as they walk with or without a cane. Looking down with their posture hunched forward, they may not only be enhancing thoughts and feelings of the past and restricting imaginings on the future, but they may find it harder to feel uplifted. In finding it harder to feel uplifted, they will likely reach for less elevating memories and a negative spiral can ensue. For them, this is not helped by self-directed neuroplasticity, where over time our thoughts interfere with the growth of our neural branches.

So... aside from helping them with some gentle posture exercises, maybe we could create environments that have the elderly looking up a little more often? Aid the possibility for positive change via the environment, beyond usual reasoning on design?

Naturally there is merit in all of us noting how we hold ourselves and how our room holds us; it is influencing our focus and experience.

Look around your room, how and where is your attention drawn?

7.

Imagination

What we are finding is that we see with our interpretative brain. This may seem like an obvious statement, except we tend to think of the eyes as the window via which we perceive what is surrounding us objectively. It is assumed that our eyes are a device for perspective to help us navigate our environment, while our brain sifts through its filing system for associations to attach meaning. What we find is that, we see what we 'rationally imagine' with our brain as the observer.

Acknowledging that we 'perceive' with our interpretative brain makes it easier to grasp how, via emotive-led reasoning, we each bring our history and circumstance with us into the process of perception. We see what we learn to see, with an observation that we are finding can even be influenced by posture and our angle of line of sight. All the while the mood-altering triggers lining our visual pathway are influencing our feeling-led reasoning, weaving an interpretation that impacts our neuroplastic system.

While all this is going on, over 10 million pieces of information are available to us every second, from which we edit to just 50. Blink. How would it be if our environment was primed to edit which 50 were given our focus, for passage through our neural gateway, and the influence that triggers? Blink.

Recall Schwartz saying that we can change the pathways of our brain by interfering with and stimulating different thoughts. How and what we edit, influences our ongoing focus, and our ongoing thoughts. If we plant meaningful associations in the design of our environment, over time we influence our responses in line with the installed narrative.

Our system is being influenced to edit what is offered through the neural gateway. Blink.

I ought to mention at this stage that though I refer to harnessing life enhancing design, there is a dilemma with a suggestible system like ours. Our system will go either way, towards vitality or away from it. If atrophy has a context in our environment, that could inhibit our potential vitality. In a neural design such as ours, our room becomes an extension of our system.

We may be willing to accept the eyes as an extension of our brain, but there may be some resistance to the idea that our room and its narrative can become one, so let us reflect on some further studies.

I mentioned that the Harvard trial was repeated in 2010. This was for the BBC documentary, The Young Ones. It was based on Professor Langer's original research that had belatedly been published as a book in 2009. The format of the programme was set up to follow most of her original guidelines, this time it was with a group of elderly celebrities. As an added dimension, the producers replicated the decor of the participants bedrooms, from 20 years before. After just one week the results were as phenomenal as they had been at Harvard. The majority doubled their stamina and manual dexterity, memory was enhanced and visual thresholds reversed. Vision improved, and some even discarded their walking sticks. It didn't just temporarily affect their mood and focus, it affected them at the cellular level. Yet, despite the programme being broadcast to millions on prime-time TV, there was hardly any comment from the press; either at the time, or since.

One would think with our quest for revitalising elixirs, and the amount spent on the promise of youth with potions and cosmetic surgery, that a few amongst the millions of us who watched would have taken note. Recall Kandel's research and our inbuilt resistance to the unfamiliar, especially if it requires a change to our core beliefs. Our assumptions of age producing atrophy and decline run deep, this programme required us to re-evaluate that perspective. It did not reference much contemporary research, which might have helped us build a context for an otherwise unfamiliar concept; we resisted and passed it by – millions of us passed it by.

8.

Spatial Mapping

I mentioned an early influence for me was the architect Richard Neutra. In his time he was as celebrated as Frank Lloyd Wright. Well known for his design prowess in the international modernist style, Neutra's work inspires architectural students to this day. What he is less well known for, are his early ideas which today would be recognised in cognitive psychology. He was interested in how we think, perceive and transform information while in our environment. He had a long list of psychologically biased questions prepared for his clients, these were to ascertain a meaningful foundation for the ensuing design.

The philosophy of phenomenology was of particular interest to him, especially occular phenomenology. In the absence of scientific data, this offered a way of informing ones subjective experience of a building; it reflected on the sensory properties of materials and the subjectivity of form and perception. Neutra was influenced in this by the writings of Maurice Merleau–Ponty who had written, *The Philosophy of Phenomenology*. He offered philosophical theories to underpin the concept that: *'that which is perceived is entangled with the body'.*

In my own early years of research, phenomenology helped me develop a lateral understanding of the impact of an environment. All manner of scientific research is now available on the internet, but in the early days this was not the case. There was limited access to studies on neurology, neurobiology and the neurocognitive sciences that bore any relation to the designed environment. If a neuroscience paper touched on design at all, it was usually towards aesthetics in general, rather than architecture in particular. By studying phenomenology and other principles, including that of proprioception, parallax and the haptic realm, I was able to expand my view.

The process of proprioception informs us of our spatial mapping and where our body is in space. Along with tensegrity [which is about the subtle balancing of the body] it allows us to make unconscious adjustments as required, so as to maintain a sense of balance and uprightness. Anyone who has had a drink/drive test where the police required them to touch their nose with their index finger and walk in a straight line, were having their mind body co-ordinates tested. They were using proprioception in an attempt to co-ordinate their body through space – to illustrate how sober they were! Parallax offered me some insight into the effect of moving through a building and its changing perspectives of the horizontal and vertical lines, as well as the shapes created by the ceilings, floors and walls as one passes through. Its focus is on how these different planes manoeuvre in and out of ones visual field, impacting ones experience as observer and response corporeally. The haptic realm is mostly about touch, though it also feeds into balance and positional awareness.

With all these I learnt that the body is ever busy telling the brain, which it is an extension of, how it is positioned. That spatial experience then informs our physical experience, going on to affect our thoughts and feelings. In the absence of more measured evidence, some understanding of this helped my research in the early days. It illuminated something of how in hanging our head, it can be harder to feel uplifted; and in holding our head and shoulders upright, it can be more difficult to feel sad.

Whether we are looking up, down, right or left, if how we hold ourselves affects our mood, and our environment affects how we hold ourselves, then the form of our surroundings has impact, as well as its resident narrative. There is a link between the physical body and non physical states, cognition and perception, today we can measure it.

With proprioception, if we simply look at a chair, we become instantly aware of its shape, size and location. Thanks to technology, we now know parts of our system are immediately preparing for the movement that would be required 'if' we were to decide to move it. When repositioning a chair at a table, that chair is moving in a place in our brain, today we can track it. If we decide to move a personal possession such as an ornament, not only does it then move in a space inside our brain, but along with the ensuing motor reflexes, there are all manner of associations going on. Who gave it, when and why, along with all the related feelings. There is a continual input of information between mind and body.

I mentioned we edit our focus to 50 pieces of information per second, from an overall option on 10 million. In the process of vision these are deconstructed then reconstructed, having been imbued with emotive-led reasoning, within 1/300th second. A process within which we bridge the gap, editing out the blurred bits, the blinds spots and our blinking.

Our system is brilliant. On entering a room, we can identify the content along with associated context and meaning in a split second glance, faster than any computer. Scientists now know that the time required for impulses to pass from one neuron to another, is many times slower than the time required by a mechanical computer to spin through a program. Yet, even with our comparatively dawdling bioneurochemical mechanism, our brain is able to make complex judgements faster, more creatively and intelligently than a network of computers. This is in part because much of our system operates many units of information at once.

No surprise that the military are plugging into our brain. They have found that when examining a site map in search of enemy hideouts, the human eye, in union with our brain, can scan these maps and intuit the relevant locations more effectively than a computer. By wearing an electrode helmet the military personnel are able to eliminate the irrelevant information and transfer the resulting relevant neural signals as co-ordinates to a computer for reference. For this, near on 100 trillion cells synchronise to carry out over 100,000 different activities. With our cross-model mechanism, simultaneous functions, and that insight in the gap between all the above, our system is a phenomenon.

We plug into this potential every moment. If we strategically manipulate a design to help us focus on a particular edit of those 50 pieces of information/second, we would be working in synergy with our neural design.

When it comes to our room and how we edit our focus there, neuroscientist Professor Vilayanur Ramachandran proposes, *'there may be much going on simultaneously as we enter a room, but as we funnel our focus, some elements draw more attention than others.'* Subtle shifts in emphasis change our experience, the sentence below illustrates this. Repeated 4 times, note how each time we change the word that has emphasis, the inference of the whole sentence changes.

I did '**not**' say I disagreed with my partner's design choice.
I did not say '**I**' disagreed with my partner's design choice.
 I did not say I '**disagreed**' with my partner's design choice.
I did not say I disagreed with my '**partner's**' design choice.

As our system responds to our environment, its emphasis funnels our focus. There the strategically installed co-ordinates can influence us as they gain access at our neural gateway.

DECONSTRUCTION + RECONSTRUCTION
+ FEELING-LED REASONING
+ IMAGINATION + MOOD ALTERERS
+ LINE OF SIGHT + POSTURE
+ PROPRIOCEPTION + EMPHASIS
+ SIMULTANEOUS FUNCTION
+ NEUROPLASTICITY

≈ SELF DIRECTED NEUROPLASTICITY
+ PERCEPTION + LEFT AND RIGHT BRAIN
+ STORY + RELEVANCE + CONTEXT
X 1/300 SEC

≈ MIND-BENDING, CELL REJUVENATING
REGENERATING, LIFE-ENHANCING
ARCHITECTURE AND DESIGN

9.

In the pink

In our frenetic world where our system is ever busy, many researchers studying the seat of consciousness are promoting the benefits of mindful meditation. The emerging view is that such contemplation offers the brain a 'conscious' rest in amongst the daily mayhem, a rest that differs to sleep.

In the commercial arena we are familiar with brain storming rooms, what might a brain calming experience be like? A space that has one focusing on deep inner stillness, while continuing to be a high-energy participant; a slowing down while still at speed. We know that the wavelength of pink light stimulates the adrenal glands in a way that secretes norepinephrine. This is a hormone that calms the system, while simultaneously sharpening one's thinking. We could illuminate a room with pink light while Mozart's Piano Sonata in D major plays in the background. This music, in particular, helped students to perform better, the researchers refered to it as the 'Mozart effect'.

For some time we have known that curves have a calming effect, and sharp angles the opposite, yet comparatively few buildings integrate curves for this purpose; not even in hospitals and prisons where they could be of great benefit. Rooms painted pink have been found to have a calming effect. One might then think, if not pink lighting then the odd pink wall would be de rigueur in prisons housing violent inmates. However it is still remarkably rare for such an institution to consider using them, let alone a union of both pink and curves to maximise a stress-reducing effect.

That said, there have been a few pioneers. In 2007 a prison in Switzerland painted 30 of its cells pink. Anger levels of troublesome inmates placed in these cells reduced within 15 minutes. In Iowa USA, a coach at Kinnick Stadium had the visiting teams' locker room painted pink. To this day there is outrage, not because they are concerned with exhibiting poor gamesmanship towards a visiting team, most haven't caught on to that. The furore is based on old views of pink being a feminine colour, as such it is considered an insult for the visiting male team. The members are reacting to a psychological assumption, rather than spotting the neurobiochemical possibility.

□ □

In light of the information unfolding here, some of it available for over a decade, it is curious that the role of cognition is not emphasized more in popular design practice. With Neutra, it is his aesthetic prowess that is revered by today's young students of design rather than his interest in the psyche. His now famous Health House, built in 1928, put him on the celebrity map and the cover of *Time Magazine*. The physician, Philip Lovell specially commissioned him for this project because he recognised all the benefits Neutra would bring, including a bias to the psyche and wellbeing. There is a clue in the name – The 'Health House'.

The 'Health House', 1928

When it comes to room as more than mere shelter, the eager young minds in architecture seem to prefer to reflect on Neutra's interest in phenomenology, rather than his bias to cognitive psychology. Preferring to engage in the poetry and intellect of philosophy. This may have much to do with Kandel's observations on our need for information to become familiar before we embrace it. The omission of neuroscience from the curriculums of most architectural schools may be for the same reason. Yet, with new insights, cognitive psychology touches on something so profound as to offer up a form of poetry – a poetry of us. This combined with an increased understanding of what it means to be human via a work of architecture, is surely worth embracing as we look to the future.

10.

Its in the genes... or is it?

Architecture and design are revealing themselves to be amongst the finest of art forms. Not simply because our buildings can be objects of beauty and offer shelter as well as nurture, but because they serve our evolutionary path. Quite literally.

Epigeneticists have found that our environments can affect our gene expression, and that of our offspring. In studying identical twins they found that if they develop in separate environments, their gene expression differs. This of course involves the wider environment, as well as the impact of one's overall lifestyle.

Within each gene is a set of instructions for making molecules that are essential to our survival. Individual genes can be switched 'on' or 'off' according to the needs and circumstances of the cell at a particular time, they can be regulated. We have assumed our genes to be an inherited code, but it turns out that over time, they can alter their expression in response to our surroundings. The old debate on nature or nurture is seemingly – nature and nurture.

□ □

As a feeling, reasoning body of associating cells, via our cross-modal system, we are able to assimilate the shape of an idea before us, and build a structure around it. As we do so, bridging the psychological, the physical, cognition and perception, even word associations impact our suggestible system. Professor John Bharge did a trial with some young university students and found they s...l...o...w...e...d down if focusing on sentences containing geriatric associations, words like elderly or sedate. If such words are represented through symbolic imagery, internal mechanisms kick in, affecting muscle action – we slow down. Neuroscientist Professor Antonio Damasio proposed that; 'the action of words on the brain evoke non verbal images that hold meaning – along with the associations that come to bear in that moment.'

If we build structures around the shape of an idea before us, and associations come to bear in the moment, what forms of structures and associations are we presenting to the elderly in care homes? There the infirm often sit in rows watching others who are inactive and infirm, day in – day out? If our environment acts as a chrysalis for change, and if we neurally intuit references more effectively than a computer, are we encouraging atrophy for our sages instead of health and healing? We now know that beauty boosts the immune system and increases our tolerance of pain; where in these care homes is the beauty, so relevant at such times in such places? What kind of chrysalis is being offered for the resident's seemingly ever more abandoned butterfly?

Let us apply this emerging knowledge for the benefit of the more vulnerable. Perhaps, in their rooms, we could lower the window ledges to the floor, and affix cantilevered faux juliette balconies filled with plants. As a fake exit it is safe, and being verdant, it gives the illusion of one being able to step into nature's glory;

playing with the neural pathways shared by the real and the imagined. In Japan research has found that a verdant view enhances ones recovery rate and wellness.

There are various ways to create a nourishing experience in our environments; from the needs of the elderly in a care home, to a baby in a maternity ward and all life's variations in-between. Neuroscientists have found that the general lighting and noise on a maternity ward detrimentally affects the development of our newborn. Since we forever renew and reorganise our cells, we are all like newborns. Lighting, shape and form has impact on us all.

Beauty also has a profound influence on us. The beauty of a sunset is not only offering a backdrop for romance, it has impact on the region of the brain associated with emotional states of romantic love. In addition, Professor Zemir Zeki found that when his participants were looking at beauty in art, there was high activity in that same region of the brain's limbic system.

As far back as the 1950s, clues were emerging on the impact of beauty. In a simple low tech experiment, the renowned psychologist Professor Abraham Maslow took three rooms and furnished them as the ugly, the average and the beautiful. In each he hung the same portraits, he wanted to see if visitors in the different settings felt the portraits projected 'well being' or not. The beautiful room was dressed with works of art and fine furniture, and though there was a large window, the illumination was calculatingly subdued. The ugly room by contrast was cluttered and painted grey. Torn light shades with over-bright bulbs hung from the ceiling and odd bits of furnishings were strewn across the floor. The average room was neat and clean and presented no real personality.

They had supervisors in each room, and as the visitors walked through it was found that what the supervisors and visitors' experienced, varied from one room to the next, yet in a similar fashion. Visitors felt the portraits hung on the walls in the ugly room seemed tired, the supervisors generally felt irritable there. In the beautiful room the visitors found the same portraits vibrant, there the supervisors were relaxed. The average room recorded only slightly better results than the ugly one.

50 years later Professor Zeki did a similar study. With the benefit of modern technology, he found that the ugly paintings activated the motor cortex. The motor cortex fires for movement. In Maslow's study the supervisors felt irritable in the ugly room and the visitors felt tired there, suggesting that ugliness could motivate one to leave.

What happens to those residents in a nursing home who cannot walk away from their sense of an 'ugly' experience, and who sit watching row, upon inactive row, of other elderly and infirm? If their motor cortex is activated, but they are confined to a chair through health issues, what implications might this have as their anxiety increases and feedback feeds back? As well as the fact that, due to our neural design, one might suppose that the impact of looking across a room with catheters, commodes and emergency oxygen on display, would cause some of them to 'buy in' to atrophy and illness.

It is no real surprise that the level of depression is 3 to 4 times higher amongst residents in a care home, than for those living with the aid of carers in the community. Apart from anything else, witnessing atrophy, triggers atrophy; witnessing vitality enhances the potential for vitality. Feeling vital, triggers more of the same, ours is a feedback system, it goes both ways, towards wellbeing or away from it. If an environment is depressing it can trigger erroneous cellular change, by contrast we know from the Harvard trial it can also trigger nurturing change. A simple improvement is to replace the pervading scent of atrophy and disinfectant with the scent of life. Metaphorically, and in real terms. If free from pesticides and distilled in steam, essential oils soothe the tissues in the brain and have a positive effect on the region of the brain involved in memory and emotions, while also diffusing a delightful scent. A simple feelgood solution to work alongside other possibilities.

Let us be meta-creative with our environments so that they act as nurturing incubators, promoting beneficial responses. There are traditional design principles, such as psychology of design and ergonomics, that can be applied to enhance one's experience. However it is with our developing understanding of the links between the physical body, non-physical states, cognition and perception, along with imagination, feelings, and an awareness of our neuroplasticity, that we can harness major benefits. We can create environments that don't just prevent atrophy, but actively encourage regeneration.

Knowing that story is our neural currency, we can create a life enhancing experience via design. We all have an imagination that feeds, and is fed by story, irrespective of age.

11.

'The map is not the territory'

Alfred Korsybski

We have tended to think of the brain as an information processor, where information goes in and comes out. Input and output. Today we understand that the input does not just go into a file for recall, it contributes to the development of our brain maps. These hold the patterns of our habitual ways of perceiving life and its events. As new input is continually evaluated against old, the development of our maps is an ever modifying process.

Our system is competitive, as specific connections increase, the maps that are fed prevail, reinforcing certain neural patterns. If we put enough life affirming information into such a system, the developing maps are influenced towards that bias as change. However, ours is a two way feedback system. If we create an environment with depressing associations, our developing maps are influenced towards that as change.

It is via our maps and their ever changing record of information that our brain is capable of 'imaging' everything inside and outside our body. This includes the shape of our limbs and their position in space. Along with proprioception and tensegrity, our maps help us harness a sense of balance, spatial awareness and orientation; aiding our interaction with our surroundings in a more self conscious way.

Our maps contribute to a resourceful state when harnessing imagination as we look upward, and memory when we look down. They are at work making us feel more positive if we stand upright, than if our body is slumped forward. Try it. Studies have shown that, due to our posture and the mind-body connection, sitting on a hard chair at the office will allow us to make decisions faster and with more clarity, when compared with sitting in a soft chair. How we are held by our space and hold our body, affects us at many levels, even affecting behaviour.

Biologists did a study with locusts where it was found that ordinary green locusts became gregarious as a result of overcrowding in a swarm. Rubbing up against each other changed their behaviour, a change that went both ways; if isolated from the swarm they reverted back to being ordinary non-gregarious locusts. Neurotransmitters in the brain control this, the main one being serotonin, one of the substances that affects mood in humans. This neurotransmitter affects our behaviour too, and can dramatically alter our own response to overcrowded conditions .

When rebuilding a school in the south of England with particularly high levels of violence, a decision was made to surrender some classroom space in the overall design to make room for wider corridors. This was to ensure that the students less frequently 'rubbed up against each other', allowing for a more fluid passage through the building at break times. The result was a 35% reduction in violence.

If we consider our environment and its design, as more of a chrysalis for our metamorphosis than mere shelter, the ramifications go way beyond reasoned ergonomics or the psychology of design.

12.

Mirror mirror

In 1970 there was a study conducted by the physiologist Benjamin Libet, a pioneer in human consciousness. In the experiment, a group of participants were hooked up to machines that measured the electrical activity on the surface of the brain. A computer was set up to give the participants instructions; the technicians behind the scenes knew what those would be, the participants did not. The instruction was simply for them to raise their finger when asked to do so. To the researchers surprise, it was found that the part of the brain that registers the moving of the finger, was responding 400 milliseconds prior to the instruction being given. Their brains seem to be anticipating the instruction before it was given. This activity in the brain is called the readiness potential. Since Libet's early experiments there have been recordings of a readiness potential in excess of 5 seconds. If our system is primed for a response before we consciously respond, then are we primed to be primed.

Those geriatrics at Harvard were primed by their surrounding environment. They may have anticipated to feel-good from the retro-bonding experience, but cell rejuvenation was a totally unexpected benefit.

So much is going on at the neural level that we are unaware of. Just watching someone sit down, triggers the parts of our brain that would be stimulated if we ourselves were to sit down; mirror neurons are at work. The neurophysiologist Giacomo Rizzolatti was the first to report on these back in 1992.

When we see someone smile many of us automatically smile in response, we may even find ourselves yawning because we see someone yawn. As I wax lyrical here about yawning, just reading my words could trigger a yawn; mirror neurons mirroring that idea in the mind. We are responding to the shape of an idea before us; as did those participants at Harvard. John Bharge's participants slowed down in response to words relating to being elderly. Recall, Antonio Damasio proposed, *'the action of words on the brain can evoke non verbal images that hold meaning'*.

All manner of neurons are continually at work. Professor Ramachandran did a trial with a condition called phantom limb syndrome. With this, sufferers can experience pain, itching and other uncomfortable sensations in a limb that has long since been amputated. In some cases they can experience such agony in the region of the missing limb, that surgeons are willing to amputate further sections in an attempt to eliminate their trauma. It was by manipulating the neural pathways shared by the real and imagined and the function [amongst others] of mirror and motor neurons, that Ramachandran was able to come up with an ingenious solution, one that was complex in its effectiveness, yet very simple in application. He placed a sequence of mirrors in such a way that his participants were able to observe the reflection of their healthy limb, as if on the side of their amputated one. This simple visual interference did the trick. As they observed the image of the healthy arm move in the place of the amputated one, after just a few sessions, for some discomfort and pain ceased. A visual trick bridged the gap between the real and the imagined, undoing erroneous associations in their cortical maps, allowing years of neural suffering to dissolve. Through neural messaging, the imagined healed the imagined. The brain is concerned with content and context. Fed by imagination and facilitated by mood altering triggers, Ramachandran's trick was working hand in glove with the design of our system. Along with perception and the system's inbuilt drive towards equilibrium, it harnessed the process of embodied cognition, and a healthy congruence was restored.

Just as a visual trick and the story it tells could restore a healthy congruence in Ramachandran's trial, our environment and its narrative can feed us restorative references. Recall how our system is able to analyse content and associations more effectively than a computer. As trillions of neurons, either excitory or inhibitory, signal and diffuse throughout our system, we constantly seek relevant co-ordinates from our surroundings. If the narrative of the design surrounding us promotes strategic, relevant, representations, over time our cells reorganise and renew in response to that bias.

Since most of the cells in our body are replaced over a period of 7 years, we are not only designed with the ability to change, there is also constant renewal. This is a renewal that we can strategically prime, again and again.

Our environment has generally been perceived as an aesthetic expression and/or practical shelter, rather than something that can offer us a metamorphosis, but new science is proving otherwise.

With viral communication, research no longer remains in the isolation it once did. As diverse fields of study connect, new possibilities are coming to the fore.

There is the expression 'critical mass', a critical point required for change. Well we are fast approaching a new one.

A seemingly radical perspective on the influence of architecture and design is emerging.

A zeitgeist is upon us.

13.

All in
the mind

We are neural weavers in a profound feedback loop. Our experience reflects the drawing below by Escher, where the hand appears to be drawing itself. If we linger in a room embedded with a meaningful narrative, that has a personal relevance and context, over time we change in accordance with our interpretation, both real and imagined.

Drawing hands, by Escher

The following story relates to what can prevail when it comes to the imagined and ageing. It is a story that highlights the influence of one's mind from a less usual perspective.

Back in the 1960s Ram Dass was a visiting professor of psychology at Berkeley, California. He was one of the adventuresome thinkers working alongside the infamous Timothy Leary, experimenting with the hallucinogenic drug, lysergic acid diethylamide – LSD. He became well versed in the caverns of the mind, then in his late 30s he went on a different kind of mind experiment – the Guru route to India. By 1997 he had become a much-loved spiritual teacher with packed audiences around the globe. In his later years he focused on the aging process and our attitudes towards it. His passion was for the elderly to find ways to reignite their vitality, and therein lay a sad irony. Though physically and mentally vital and belying his 67 years, as he explains in the introduction to his last book, 'Still Here'; he was wondering what it would be like to be 90 years old, have failing health and be weak limbed. Having spent many years in devotional contemplation, he was adept at meditation and familiar with letting himself go with the flow of his imaginings. One day he took himself deep into meditation, imagining himself older, weaker and infirm. At some point he fell to the floor and was unable to use his limbs. Initially he thought he was still in the sensorial imaginings of his medita-tion, but then realized he was on the floor and couldn't lift himself up. He had suffered a stroke. He survived but was con-fined to a wheelchair for the rest of his life.

Where the system is capable of moving towards vitality or away from it, Ram Dass may have listened to his genuine desire to experience what it was like to be infirm and debili-tated. Perhaps his skill at meditation and his gift for accessing deep sensorial imaginings, caused his system to respond in accordance with his focused imaginings. If we consider the role played by mood altering substances, real and imagined sharing similar pathways and self-directed neuroplasticity, he might not so much have bypassed the protocols of the system, as harnessed them – but erroneously? The geriatrics in the Harvard trial reflected on vitality not frailty, and they rejuve-nated within a week.

We will never know what happened for Ram Dass that day, we know he reflected on failing health and being weak limbed. We also know the mind as a process is a powerful mechanism.

Where reasoning leads feelings, and they in turn are fed by our imagination, our interpretation of reality and our experience is often based on a 'seeming logic'. I say 'a seeming logic' because it is us who, through association, determine the context and relevance and influence the interpretation.

Depending on our developed expectations, even the imagined can offer up a congruence and go on to influence change.

Antonio Damasio found that when subjects imagined the sound of a guitar, patterns in their auditory cortex corresponded to what they heard in their 'mind's ear' – as if real. Some individuals with pollen sensitivity sneeze upon seeing a plastic flower, it depends on the context. A plastic rose lying on a tray in the bathroom may have little noticeable effect, but a plastic rose upright in a vase on a window ledge can trigger a critical shift in neural activity. For some asthmatics, just seeing a rose upright in a vase can trigger the release of histamine. The imagined crossing over as real. Thus, extending a window in a care home so it reaches to the floor, and adding a faux balcony, can create a sense of accessible space beyond the confines of a room. Along with all the benefits that engenders.

If we offer the imagined a context, as if real, we enable a sensorial crossover. We are meaning-makers, it is us that make it real.

At Harvard they were aware it wasn't the 50s of their youth. However, the harnessing of their emotive-led reasoning woven with their imagination, triggered sufficient references to their younger years, to achieve very real results. Senses crossed-over and via interpretation and neuroplasticity, the imagined hitched a ride on their potential for renewal.

There is no magic at work, no need to attach esoteric principles; this is how we are designed. Our system has a mechanism that offers an alchemy worthy of Merlin, we are just not familiar with it.

> Daily we build structures around ideas,
> and as meaning-makers,
> we make them real.

In the 1940s, psychologist Mary Ann Simmel produced a simple film that involved moving geometric shapes around on a piece of paper. A circle moved around while a couple of triangles and a rectangle opened and closed at one end. When the film was shown to an audience, they imagined all sorts of accompanying narratives, animating their form with emotion. With our tendency to story, some shapes were perceived to be stealing the circle, others to be in love! How might we respond to the shapes in our environment? What story might they tell if one purposefully moves them around, as one does in meaningful design?

We normally have some kind of narrative in mind when we come up with a design concept. For some it may be inspired by a special place discovered while travelling, a retro concept perhaps, a display in a designer's showroom or a magazine article. As we integrate our narrative of choice into the design, we are moving ideas around to which we have attached emotions. If the narrative is deeply meaningful, so is our attachment.

Some contemporary fields of cognitive study, recognise that we can associate an emotionally charged experience with a particular shape, colour and texture, even its temperature and scent. These associations act as a form of symbolic reference. If we then change any of them in a way that harnesses new 'meaningful' references, something alters in our attached emotional charge. Image and meaning are presenting as one story, told in terms of the other. If we then change one at a meaningful level, we change the other.

For example, if a glowing cobalt blue cube comes to mind when reflecting on a traumatic experience, that cube becomes a metaphor for that emotive story. It may be a story that, due to trauma, we do not have words for, but we have the form and its sensations. In then changing those in a way that harnesses new meaning, perhaps the colour changes or the brightness, something changes in the emotional charge we attach to it. In therapy this is referred to as embodied cognition. If facilitated well, it can offer a motorway route to emotional freedom. Ramachandran's mirror box offered a form of embodied cognition for those amputees, liberating them from years of suffering. Image and meaning came together to undo a trick, without language and misinterpretation getting in the way.

By the nature of our design, if we weave a strategic narrative into our environment, that has relevant life enhancing associations, as we incubate there, we stimulate the attached emotions.

14.

Welcome
to the new

Though Kandel proposed that information needs to be repeatedly laid down to memory before we can digest it, and we tend to reach for the familiar, ultimately, we are wired for the new! Neuroscientists Biederman and Vessel found that as information is repeated, activity in the opioid rich areas lessens, and our chemical reward reduces. This appearing paradox offers a synergy that works well in terms of our development, for as information becomes familiar and the chemical rush reduces, we seek the next new. As a consequence of continually reaching for the new, we are necessarily creating the next familiar; then as one chemical rush subsides, we seek the next high, and so on. It benefits our evolution to seek the next new, even as we hold on to the old and familiar along the way, it allows us to make comparisons and discerned choices.

Despite our tendency to reach for the familiar, in our competitive system, the new will ultimately win. However, it can be a challenge to reach for the new, for many reasons. One of them is that we tend to approach the new via the familiar, and that is fed by the past, for it already has context, relevance and expectations attached. And since we tend to see what we have learnt to see, our interpretation is often what we expect. Feeding us back into the same old, same old; the system is tricky.

Learning how our system works from diverse angles here, is enabling us to make new neural connections in relation to the information. Via our feedback system, the ideas can become familiar.

Recall what Schopenhauer said of the truth:
1st – it is ridiculed.
2nd – it is violently opposed.
3rd – it is accepted as being self-evident.

The celebrated 20th century lateral thinker Edward De Bono said; 'For hundreds of years we have believed if something is logical in hindsight, then logic should have been enough to get the idea in the first place.' Inferring this is not so, he suggests that we in fact require an informed gestation period before we 'get it'. Kandel's work on memory confirms this, and the over-looking of the results at the Harvard trial and the BBC documentary helps to illustrate it.

Here the studies I have referred to, like the one at Harvard and those by Ulrich, Bharge, Damasio, Kandel, Schwartz and Ramachandran, are contributing to that gestation. They are repeated to reinforce that. The linking references such as eye movement, cognition, mood altering triggers, the readiness potential, mirror neurons and more, add to this. Pieces of a puzzle fall into place, and we begin to grasp the less familiar and expand our expectations.

Many of us will have noticed when doing a picture puzzle, that once enough pieces are in place, we achieve an accelerated ability to judge where the remaining ones fit. These studies contribute to that, they act as a point of reference, simplifying the otherwise complex and less familiar. As the information expands our expectations, a space for a radical new perspective on design opens up. That zeitgeist I mentioned!

The overall information
becomes familiar,
enough for it to become
ordinary.

15.

In the eye of the beholder

Today we have evidence that our environment can be manipulated to nurture us, beyond our previous imaginings. Epigeneticists are informing us that patterns of inheritance are programmed to be influenced by our environment. With this the impact of architecture goes beyond offering mere shelter, beauty and the nurturing of our neurological development; it may yet prove to be one of the greatest of art forms. If it can influence our gene expression, it is certainly touching the art of being human.

When delivering his now famous hierarchy of needs, Professor Maslow endeavoured to unravel something of what it means to be human. In the revision of his classic, *Motivation and Personality* [1970], he added aesthetic/beauty to his short list of 7 needs (physiological, safety, belonging & love, esteem, self-actualization, to understand/to know, aesthetics/beauty).

Whatever our human need for beauty, in our environment it plays a significant part, it boosts our immune system, raises our pain threshold and triggers romance. These are surely reasons enough to harness it. Many of us will have heard the expression that beauty is 'in the eye of the beholder', well it is – literally. It is in our DNA and wired into our brain.

In 2007 Rizzolatti, the first to report on mirror neurons, did a study on beauty with his team in Parma. Using functional magnetic resonance imaging [fMRI] they mapped the area of the brain that relates to art appreciation, while showing their subjects images of a renaissance sculpture – Polykleitos's Doryphoros – in various proportions. Proportion was used as an independent variable to isolate it from other influences. They found the insular, a region of the brain that responds to beautiful images, was particularly stimulated when the image had a ratio of 1:0.618. This is a mathematical proportion that in ancient times was referred to as the golden ratio. Centuries ago, the mathematician Pythagoras believed that wherever you found this ratio you found great 'beauty'. However, prior to 2007 such claims would have been an insightful but unfounded mystical idea.

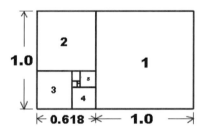

The golden ratio

In mathematics, the ratio relates to the Fibonacci sequence of numbers illustrated below. This is a sequence whereby, whatever the first two numbers, each subsequent number is the sum of the previous two.

1,2,3,5,8,13,21

The Fibonacci sequence

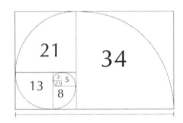

The Fibonacci sequence is used in computer algorithms, as well as being found in patterns that weave throughout our natural world. Fractals. 30 years ago fractal patterns were examined by the mathematician Benoit Mandelbrot, they were found in snowflakes, cloud formation, lightning and more.

Fractal patterns

Where there is a pattern in the Fibonacci sequence, whereby the numbers that come before, reflect in the numbers that come after, it is similar with fractals. Mandelbrot found that the more one magnified a fractal pattern, the more the structure within appeared the same. Patterns within patterns, they weave and are then woven.

If one analyses the patterns of the fractals on the leaf of an oak tree, one can predict the shape the tree will become. The patterns are predictive, enough to be used on the trading floors of Wall St. There, fractal graphs are used to anticipate the commercial markets. Anthropologists use them when examining the rise and fall of civilisations.

Fractal patterns have been found in our ever-expanding universe, the particle field and our biological beginnings, they are in our DNA and the folds of our brain. A mysterious mathematics connecting the commercial arena, the celestial one, nature, our cerebral workings and ... beauty.

Beauty has a formula,
and its proportion is a
pattern of numbers ... woven into our DNA!

For many less familiar reasons, it may be worth integrating our personal sense of beauty into our environment, where it can trigger more than pure aesthetics.

Whether based on principles of pure mathematics or nature, pattern and form are integral parts of our existence. So it was only a matter of time before we began to explore them using computer technology.

Many architects and designers are excited today by computer generated 3D design. Often combining shapes, angles and perspectives which contradict accepted conventions, these buildings, at full scale, can seem to defy gravity. However, if our environment functions more as a metamorphic chrysalis than as a shell for a snail, and these are complex forms that only a computer can configure, perhaps we first need to explore the new evidence on the brain – in case, in our enthusiasm, we are overlooking something. For the challenge is not in the structural engineering, as we are continually developing innovative solutions, it has more to do with their impact on our neural engineering and how we may adapt in response. Additionally in neuropsychiatry, they propose that what the mind can conceive it can believe. If the forms of these 3D models are so complex that only a computer can configure them, forms we humans cannot conceive, [with reference to cognition] when we are in their full-scale built structures – can we really believe them?

However exciting and elegant some of their geometry may appear, might these environments offer a less meaningful experience for a system like ours. Would we feel like visitors in them, instead of part of an organic experience. These are questions worth asking as we develop our future city and townscapes. We need to be aware of the human experience, and how we function neurologically, especially in light of emerging evidence from epigenetics.

Broad Museum by Zaha Hadid

There is much at work as our buildings come to life in synergy with our alchemy. Sixty years ago Merleau-Ponty could only theorise on, 'the system of experience' where, 'that which is perceived is entangled with the body'; today we can more easily measure it.

With architecture still isolated from the general sciences and their groundbreaking evidence, we can easily overlook some of the ramifications of new architectural ideas in the excitement of inventing them. Although we don't want to hold back the frontiers of innovation, we do need to reflect on the cons as well as the pros.

Science has opened a lid on a treasure trove, good and bad; we can't close it now. We can't pretend not to know about some of the emerging possibilities, we just need to consider what we create from a less familiar perspective.

Our previous concerns have been with sustainability and eco issues. Knowing neural change in response to the surrounding environment can happen for us all in a blink, and even influence our gene expression; it is time to consider the ramifications of 'neural issues'.

> In a man-made environment
> we are, in part at least,
> mind-made.

16.

Virtual room

The various areas of study mentioned so far might appear, to us lay people, to be beyond the scope of our daily lives, but the evidence trickles down to us in the way we experience our environments. Never more so than in our own personal surroundings, where we linger and are more attached to the narrative. So we cannot absolve ourselves of some sense of responsible curiosity. At our inexpert level, the arena of cognitive psychology can offer access to processes we could harness to our benefit, via strategic design choices.

In the commercial arena of virtual gaming, they use the principles of cognitive psychology when monitoring our virtual room experience. They assess the making of emotive features by recording our response as audience, to realities created by the game. For this they use electroencephalography [EEG] and fMRIs to measure the electrical fields on the surface of the brain associated with excitatory and inhibitory activity. Where we are the audience for their game, in our personal room we are the audience too, as well as being a character immersed in the narrative we are observing. The room without, is projected inside our brain. There it triggers all manner of signals of exciting and inhibiting activity, these diffuse throughout our system as an electrochemical story.

What story might hoarders be weaving? Their internal synopsis is reflected in their environment, packed floor to ceiling, wall-to-wall, with junk. Junk they 'perceive' as treasure. Broken radios found on the street, random pieces of plastic, old newspapers and clothes piled everywhere. All kinds of objects they believe they may one day repair or find a use for! It is a behaviour considered to be a clinical condition. There are many of us with a less usual emotional attachment to our 'stuff', and a less usual interpretation of what it means to us. The UK's Institute of Psychiatry suggests that 5% of the population are officially hoarders, the same proportion occurs in the USA. This equates to over 15 million people in the United States who have some inner turmoil reflected in this way.

The fashion for renting storage lockups is a less overt version; it depends on the unnecessary excesses we are storing and the length of time we store them. For the 95% of us not 'officially' considered hoarders, it is worth considering letting our excess go.

Even a storage unit around the corner becomes an extension of us, and our environment. We do not forget about our stuff, however far away, it is filling an emotional gap, consciously or not. Mostly we find that if it is worthy of story, we are attached; and if it is not worthy of a story we would not be keeping it. So if it is stored, even around the corner, we are probably attached.

There are places in our brain where we retain references to our 'stuff'. Ever noticed having moved the toaster, going back to where it used to be... again and again; so ingrained is its old position in our neural theatre? Our mechanism of proprioception, that helps identify the location of our body in space, is involved in the location of objects too, including that toaster. When proprioceptive learning and perception weave together, they serve us well. We can attend a lecture, and as the speaker refers to a place on the stage to symbolize something, that particular place represents that area of his topic. As he repeatedly refers to it, we hold it spatially in our mind, if he points elsewhere with reference to it, it can be confusing.

When it comes to objects located in space and their meaning, 'stuff' stored around the corner also has a place of reference for us? Out of sight may not be out of mind. Each of us is the best judge of whether we are hoarding, storing or reminiscing. It is always down to personal interpretation. Interpretation that is conjured by mood-altering triggers, feeling-led reasoning and our imagination-inspired brain.

We are a meaning-making system and perception is very different to seeing.

17.

Meaning makers

The Langley Porter experiments illustrated that eye movements were intrinsically linked with neurological processes. Wundt referred to the muscles of the eye being connected to the muscles of the head. Over a century ago he said, 'if the eye is involuntarily drawn to see something, this will trigger the head to turn towards that visual stimuli, which will in turn change the direction the entire body is moving'. This may seem logical enough, but we now recognise how neurophysiologically complex such a simple sequence is; and understand some of the ramifications. Looking upwards offers a resourceful state for focusing on the future, as imagination weaves with visual constructs, whereas if our gaze is lowered, we access feelings and memories. How a building influences our gaze as we pass through, affects us.

There are all manner of surrounding influences that we over-look. Have you ever noticed a tendency to lower your voice if the lights in a room are dimmed; an internal dialogue is at work, one that even random shapes can trigger. Different to Simmel's film, where shapes move around on a piece of paper inspiring various narratives; or a shape such as a red triangle when, depending on one's culture, it might tell the story – 'CAUTION'. I mean an abstract shape that is apparently free of associations or any related theatre.

Take a look at the two shapes below and the two made up words 'Bouba' and 'Kiki' alongside them. Make a note of which shape best reflects each word for you.

Bouba
Kiki

In tests, 98% said Bouba reflected the curved shape and Kiki the jagged one; you possibly found the same. There is a sensor-ial crossover. Bouba, a made up word, triggers signals that offer the story of a softer form. Even random shapes offer a story for our interpretative system, it is all about story.

With Ramachandran's mirror box, where trauma confused the system, a visual trick relieved it. It triggered a story attached to a congruence deep within the system's intelligence, as could the blue cube and its associations. Our system is an interde-pendent neurobiochemical piece of wondrous theatre.

If we rearrange the interior of our room in a 'meaning-filled' fashion, that taps representations deep within, the resultant story harnesses attached emotions, changing us. However, we will not arbitrarily change in response to the surrounding story. As with the participants at Harvard, there has to be relevance and context, even though we are the ones who determine what that is. As I said, the system is tricky.

□ □

It is worth noting in this meaning-making tricky system of ours, that if we neglect to impose 'preferred meaning' in our surroundings, and negative references remain, the resident meaning will impose itself on us. If there is relevance and context, our system will respond, good and bad.

□ □

Some of us may declare that our space is simply the work of a designer, or the previous tenant; that we just happened to step into its display. In this, we may assume that we are divorced from its impact, but if we don't then personally alter it, there is some resonance going on – or there will be. It is in our design to respond. Look around, does your room's narrative serve you?

> Consider the story your surroundings may
> be telling of you, and your yesterdays,
> they are projecting into your future.

18.

Puzzle parts

Jonas Salk, who invented the vaccine for Polio, recognised the value of working in a laboratory specifically designed to inspire. In 1986 he commissioned Louis Kahn to create just such a building, the award winning Salk Research Institute in San Diego was the result.

Salk Institute, San Diego

Salk himself was initially researching in a basement laboratory. Uninspired, he credits his trip to a monastery in Assisi and the beauty there, as the moment of inspiration for his vaccine. That said, the majority of research is carried out in windowless rooms, often devoid of personality, packed with machines and distracting background noise. The latter being of concern for many reasons. I mentioned that the general lighting and noise on maternity wards detrimentally affects the development of newborn babies. With such an effect on our biological processes, what impact could they be having on experimental cell cultures. The overall environment is influencing the researchers, and what they are incubating; the results of which become the foundation of future research. Research that may, or may not go on to serve them and us.

□□

As researchers go from one project to another, endeavouring to fire up new inspiration and seek tenure, they cross many diverse fields. Edward Vessel, who investigated the mood altering triggers along the visual pathway, went on to study our response to aesthetics in Art. His research colleague, Irving Biederman, chose the arena of face recognition. Aesthetics would seem to have an obvious connection with architecture and design, and yet surprisingly so does face recognition. Biederman found that our brain works much like a detective with an identikit, ever seeking a match from amongst its files. As information comes in, we build an image via association, memory and context; facial fragments such as a nose, an eye or the turn of a brow are identified as parts of a puzzle. Remembered features fall into place through association and from these we build a whole; this is how we recognise someone just from the curl of their lip.

When recognizing a building, we do a variation of this. As we look at its roof line, facade, windows, height, orientation and materials, information and associations are pulled in from different regions of the brain. Similarly in our personal room, with its narrative there is form, colour, furnishings and their associations. Different stories link up and weave with memories, imagination and more. At Harvard, the surrounding narrative fed references to memories of a more youthful time, triggering puzzle parts to fall into place, and neurons to fire in line with that.

With our personal environment, the narrative woven there can cause parts of a puzzle, otherwise obscured by forgetfulness, conditioning, time and circumstance, to fall into place. A photograph of a loved one can trigger memories and we weave these into our experience as neural firings; be that of a joyous time in our life or a sad one. Depending on the relevance for us, we ever respond. As puzzle parts fall into place and neurons fire and wire, together or apart in a sea of electrochemical activity, we grow our story, towards wellbeing or away from it. All manner of associations are at work, all the time and at many levels. Our left and right brain working in unison with feelings, imagination, reasoning and more – much more.

Even the detail of whether a surface is hard or soft contributes to our interpretation, the sensations weave with the surrounding narrative. Where one cannot define hard if one does not know soft, or light if one does not know dark, all manner of associations are triggered. Professor Damasio illustrated that in the subtleties of 'knowing soft' and its reference to hard, there is also the quality of the 'softness' of soft.

The chair we are sitting on as we read this, is not only soft or hard beneath us. If it is soft, we are aware of the softness, if it is hard, we are aware of the hardness. An awareness that is often not conscious, yet it affects our experience and neural response. Our chair and its degree of softness can affect our mood, a mood that can contribute to our wellbeing.

Sitting on a hard chair affects posture, causing some people to make clearer decisions than when sitting on a soft one. Take a moment to feel the seat beneath you, is it hard or soft? Beyond that sensation, can you sense the degree of the hardness or softness? We popularly assume the familiar 5 senses of sound, taste, touch, scent and sight, but we have over 70. We tend to overlook temperature and balance as sensory responses but they are, and we can even sense softness – beyond the level of touch.

When in a blue room, our temperature and that of the room drops more than in a red room, and time 'appears' to pass more quickly. The temperature is a literal change, not a phantom one, the reading on the room's thermostat falls. Beyond the psychological impact and the physics of colour, when time seems to pass more quickly in a blue room, not only are we responding to the room's reduced temperature, we are responding to its blueness!

In the office, the hardness of the chilled glass desk beneath the document we are signing affects us differently to the warmth and more forgiving surface of a walnut one. The detail of whether it is curved or rectangular also has impact.

The design of our office and its influence extends beyond its shapes, textures and colours, to the location of our working space with reference to colleagues we feel supported by, or not. We may prefer not to have to think about such detail all the time, but the thing is, we do respond – all the time, often unconsciously.

The Johnson Wax building by Frank Lloyd Wright, 1939

As we glance over the newly installed open plan screen dividers to a window with a view – or not, we are affected by the aspect, the surrounding images, location and ergonomics.

All of the above are in addition to the colours and shapes woven into the narrative, as well as the subtle layers of detail within the detail and the emphasis. We respond to the curvature of the curves, the level of shine to the surfaces, and the brightness of the lighting. The general narrative affects us, as well as the one that is more personal to us; all the while being aware of the nature of the business and our role in it. So, whether the new kid on the edgy block of architecture, has given our company headquarters a computer configured form, or tapped nature with an organic vertical garden in its lobby, we will respond at many neurological levels, towards well-being, or away from it.

An executive in a creative business may be closed off from inspiration by something as simple as a convex curved red wall. It may have been installed as a generic design feature with the assumption that red fires up the adrenals and curves feed the 'flow' of ideas. Curves could of course have a calming influence, which may be good in some circumstances, but imagination is being inhibited by the red, we want blue for that.

We are a feedback meaning-making system at so many levels. Expressions like 'a soft sound' or 'a loud colour' make sense to us because our senses cross over, and feedback feeds back. Say the word 'soft' in your mind and then the word 'loud', note how soft is quieter in the mind's ear. Go on, try it. The associations are crossing over, not just the syntax. Try to say 'loud' in your mind as a soft sound, difficult isn't it? One would think it is just a word, but old associations are coming to bear. Even with Bouba, it does not just have a soft sound as a reflection of its shape, as senses cross over even its volume is soft. Compare it to Kiki, try it, listen. What might be going on with the story our own environment is telling, as senses cross over and our system attempts to assimilate the input.

Consider the alchemy at work, for a neural story to trigger an accelerated recovery for those patients on the ward with a window. Their senses crossing-over as they simply lay in their bed. All manner of associations and interpretation are constantly at work, as input vies for our attention. Day-in-day-out, we are editing to the 50 pieces of information/sec that will gain access at our neural gateway. If via meaningful design, we strategically edit what those pieces might be, we are working in synergy with our neural nature.

Much of our response is about story and pattern recognition. Even Bouba and Kiki, with no attached theatre, told a story; otherwise 98% of us would not have identified Bouba as having a soft sound. We do not just read the words we respond to their shape and hear them. I mentioned that Damasio did a study where just by imagining the sound of a guitar, patterns were created in the auditory cortex that corresponded to what was heard in the 'mind's ear', as if real.

In the day-to-day, we are not simply dealing with senses crossing over where Bouba can cause us to hear a soft sound, we also know that an imagined sensation can be interpreted as real. It is in part because real and imagined share similar neural pathways and senses cross over that those amputees could suffer, and it is because of this that they could heal. Feelings, sounds, thoughts and more, criss-cross over as imagination ever weaves with interpretation. A cross-over where colour can affect taste and a red drink can taste sweeter than a green one. With the condition of synesthesia, some hear sounds when they look at numbers, others smell colours, or even taste them.

Much is going on as expectation weaves
into our interpretation.

19.

Tricks

Today the neurological sciences are sharing a dialogue across many disciplines. We have cognitive neuroscience, neurophysiology, neurobiology, neurophysics, visual psychophysics, neurolinguistics, neuropsychology and cognitive neurolinguistics, to name a few. As I researched into these disciplines, it became evident that framing a relevant story, at a deep representational level, was a means for facilitating a design method that could proactively harness our neural wonder.

To explore this and gain a deeper understanding of the persuasive power of a strategic story, I trained in hypnosis. Having previously learnt that intonation is interpreted by the right brain and syntax the left, I recognised that hypnosis could lead me to something of the qualities of tone and pacing, as well as the influence of subliminal storytelling. My intention was to uncover the equivalent in design, whereby an environment could, for example, encourage one to slow down, or the opposite. Beyond the personal, at a generic level, a financial trading company may want the environment to encourage a certain pace, while still nurturing an element of calm for the individuals in the room. I studied the influence of image, patterns of language and cognitive linguistics to expand my understanding of how we operate, always with persuasive design and its application as my focus.

When it came to studying hypnosis, I learnt that no one hypnotises us, rather we allow the hypnosis to take place. Our willingness to open to the suggestion of a hypnotist, is measured by the degree to which we allow them, to allow us to influence ourselves; we enable the process.

Up to the age of 6 we are in the theta delta hypnogogic state, and then until we die, remain susceptible to change via our soft-wiring. From the cradle to the grave the stage is set for our soft-wiring to change in line with the story we condition ourselves to imagine.

Our neural system is designed with safety protocols, relevance and context are two of them; 'self' hypnosis is another. We are the ones telling ourselves the hypnotic story, and then in turn, seducing ourselves with it. There are many tricks. It is because of the trickiness, that there is the potential for strategic design to regenerate and rejuvenate our system.

We have been designed to be capable of creating a design that can reshape the design we were designed to forge. If one catches the trick of it all?

Every day of our life there are moments where we trick ourselves; sometimes erroneously, mostly unconsciously. Why else would anorexics have a distorted perception of parts of their body whereby, as a result of starving their system, they can tragically end up killing themselves? Something they imagine hitches a ride, triggering all manner of erroneous chatter in their mind. The system responds to 'perceived' input. That mirror box triggered a positive trick for those 'phantom amputee's, relieving years of suffering as puzzle parts fell into place. Those geriatrics at Harvard tricked themselves.

When it comes to tricking the system and our room being an hypnotic facilitator for a strategic sensorial story, it is within where the alchemy happens and the story comes to life. Inside our brain, the same place where the seed of the story emerged, and where the room is reflected. Where real and imagined come together – within.

We are a meaning-making mechanism.

Our whole life is an unfolding collection of stories built on illusions fed by the imagination; all held in place by their relationship with other illusions and their stories. We are ever making them up, creating all manner of synopses that would make the finest of Hollywood proud. The wonder is the degree to which we are able to influence the unfolding neurological plot, via the 3D theatre of a strategically 'conceived' room.

20.

Illusions

Curiously, despite our brilliance, when making a decision or attempting to brainstorm a new idea, many of us experience a mental block. When this happens, it can feel like the only solution is to give up and head off for a coffee break, or something similar. Then, more often than not, just as we are distracted, inspiration finds us. Have you ever woken up in the morning, after an evening struggling over choices to be made, and suddenly a resolution comes to mind? Our right brain connects disparate information, and the answer to a prevailing problem emerges.

Professor of Psychology John Kounios and cognitive neuroscientist Mark Jung-Beeman, demonstrated that when the system is seeking a solution out of a vast sea of possibilities, it is the portal for metaphors, our storytellers, that edit out the irrelevant. Image and meaning come together for an inspired relevant solution.

Ramachandran proposes that metaphors evolved from synesthesia as babies; a pre-lingual crossing over of image and meaning. They share a portal with imagination and inspiration. With their ability to tell one story in terms of another, metaphors are indispensable for science's visionaries, helping them better imagine abstract, yet relevant ideas. It was a metaphor that inspired Einstein when he came up with the formula $E = MC^2$, he was imagining what it would be like to travel on a beam of light. Image and meaning came together as inspiration.

When E = Energy and MC^2 = mass at the speed of light in a vacuum, the story of mass is told as energy; one story told in terms of another.

Where MC^2 = E, Einstein advocated that everything in our world, all matter, exists as a dynamic vibration, oscillating subatomic particles. We may be able to touch our material world as a bulk of atoms, be that a chair or a wall, but at core the atoms are made of trillions of vibrational subatomic particles. Within each subatomic particle only 0.0001% is physical, the other 99.9999% is virtual spinning nothingness. Yet were we to examine that 0.0001% that appears physical, we would find that 99.9999% of that is virtual spinning nothingness, and in turn, the 0.0001% of that which appears physical is also 99.9999% virtual spinning nothingness... and on. An analogy would be unravelling our material world, our chair and the wall as one would a vibrational virtual Russian doll... towards virtual nothingness. Illusionary material reality, not even dust.

From spinning virtual nothingness we get our atomic experience, as a vibrational somethingness that we can touch and feel. The core of our material reality is as surreal as that of our neural one. The latter being parked inside our architectural space, that is held in the particle field. All of it – us, this and that – made of the same virtual spinning non stuff.

Inside a particle looks like this   ....
Inside a star looks like this   .....
Inside a brick looks like this   .....
Inside our brain looks like this   .....

Add that a mysterious mathematics connects the particle field, nature, beauty and our DNA, and we find ourselves woven into a vast puzzle in which the Earth's celestial illusions weave with our cerebral ones. Our senses tell us that the earth is flat and that I am sitting still, the earth is not flat and I am not sitting still. We are on board a planet that spins at 36,000 miles/hour, and we don't feel it turn. The same gravity that prevents me falling off it, with a touch of the neurological wonder of proprioception, can help me feel upright as I walk through a building. Since our walls are perpendicular to the curved surface of roundish earth, as I walk upright through that building, its walls only appear parallel, and as Einstein provocatively proposed, they only seem solid.

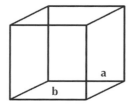

Necker cube

No surprise that there are so many tricks at so many levels. If we look at the image of the Necker cube above, and focus on the rectangle to the forefront, at some point we will note it suddenly flips. Whichever is forefront as we look at the cube, 'a or b', wait and note the other one 'flip' to the fore. This flip is only partly voluntary – it moves in our mind not in physical reality, we have to focus to see the flip. Curiously, when focus partners up with observation, we find it has an interdependence with our ability to think! This is illustrated with a simple exercise. Imagine the corner of your room down by the skirting. Either in your imagination with your eyes closed, or if you prefer with your eyes open, watching a real corner in the room – down by the skirting. Keep looking as if waiting for a mouse to come around the corner, except you are focusing on that corner for your next thought to appear. Try it – watch and wait. You will find that no thoughts arise. When you are focused on looking for them, none appear, the act of focused observation inhibits the thought process.

Observation and focus are participants in our experience at many unfamiliar levels. In the Langley Porter study, looking up and left, for the majority, tapped memory and up and right tapped visual fantasy and imagery. Earlier we learnt that inspiration emerges when we aren't focusing our thoughts, yet if we focus on what our next thoughts may be, none emerge.

Imagine proactively harnessing something of this trickiness in our everyday experience. Perhaps by utilising the cognitive process of eye movements when curating an exhibition. In a gallery one could display the works in the knowledge that someone visiting might look up and to the left or up and to the right, or strategically set it up so that they did. As a result a bias to memory or imagery could be manipulated to influence some of the visitors. We could even influence the ability to switch into non-thinking mode while there, offering a respite from our otherwise constant stream of thoughts.

When we attend the theatre for a few hours, whether we are stage left or right, different neurological processes are triggered. If we are watching a future-based fantasy play or a period piece, it will be experienced differently by some in the audience looking up to the stage from the stalls, than for others looking down from the royal circle. There is also impact in the working day at the metaphoric theatre of the office. During a meeting at an ideas company, one may be encouraged to look at a screen presentation at one end of the conference table. For some it may be up and to the right; as a result they may find themselves better inclined towards visual inspiration. Whereas their colleagues looking up and left on the other side of the table, might be more inclined towards memory. In the advertising industry it is accepted that an advert placed on a right hand page is more valuable than one on the left; there are recognised psychological principles underpinning the enhanced value. Advertising gurus selling their clients wares may wish to consider their presentation and placement of an advert, and its configuration, from a different perspective – literally.

Gosh, who wants to think like this, all the time? Well, evidently our physiology in partnership with our neurology is designed to do so, all the time, and mostly unconsciously.

21.

Shaping them
– to shape us

Chartres Cathedral, France   *Church of the Light, Osaka*

In a place of spiritual worship our real and imagined worlds come together in a fundamental way. A place where the surroundings are designed to inspire, and our mental focus drifts towards that which is beyond the human realm.

Chartres Cathedral in France, is an inspiring example. It's grand, gothic architecture and diffused lighting from the magnificent rose window, has us bathing in beauty as well as looking upward with a sense of awe. Upward to where thoughts might be enhanced towards that which is beyond our current knowing. By contrast Tadao Ando's 'Church of the light' in Osaka – Japan, is a modest modern structure. It has the sign of the cross carved out of the front wall as a glass window, floor to ceiling – wall to wall. The cross is set behind the alter, directly in front of the congregation. Though simple, it can still inspire awe as the sunlight breaks through and casts its beam as a form of the cross onto the interior. In looking straight ahead, as the sun's rays travel across this church and the congregants, might it cause one's spiritual connection to be more accessible in the present moment, compared to an experience that has one looking up to the imagined and beyond?

As neural signals televise images inside our brain, the story in any church is ultimately interpreted in a personal way; it is always personal. The same for dictators. Many have built themselves palatial environments, more often than not as a reflection of their perceived personal story on power and narcissism.

Luitpold Hall, facade by Hitler's architect Albert Speer

Saddam Hussein's Palace

If one bothers to look at the edifices they build, one might note an uneasy similarity revealed in their shared sentiment, their story within reflected without. If we consider our environment to be a mirror of self, theirs is a narrative designed to maintain and feed their delusion.

Our system has all manner of ways of determining what is personally relevant. We know the imagined sound of a guitar can trigger patterns in the auditory cortex as if real, just reading about a yawn can trigger one, and words relating to being eld-erly can slow us down. Aware of this, might there be an advan-tage at the Pentagon and other global equivalents, if the War Office was renamed the Peace Room? Especially as Damasio said, 'the action of words on the brain evoke non-verbal images that hold meaning, along with the associations that come to bear in that moment.' When it comes to the White House with its 'Oval Office', one might enquire as to whether its curves hold the leader of the free world in a less antagonistic frame of mind when making decisions.

The Oval Office at the White House

Many years ago I was invited to consult at Downing St, the United Kingdom's White House. While discussing my evolving views on design and leaning on Sir Winston Churchill's famous armchair, I was asked what he might have said about the direc-tion I was heading. Rather serendipitously I was able to quote the great man himself.

Churchill had said; *'There is no doubt whatever about the influ-ence of architecture and structure upon human character and action. We make our buildings and afterwards they make us. They regulate the course of our lives.'*

22.

Lifestyle

When it comes to buildings regulating the course of our lives, and everything being a story, there is a particular genre of architecture emerging that tells the story of our 21st century aspirations. It was born out of the recession that followed the 1980s 'aspire to acquire' phenomenon; bringing with it a noticeable bias towards lifestyle and luxury. I don't mean the fashion for bold towering structures, competing in height from one global city to another. I refer to lifestyle apartments, where brand as story has hitched a ride. I highlight these for, like us, they are specifically about story.

Many lifestyle buildings have developed over the years,
the difference for us today, is that the reach
of our aspirations has changed.

As an architectural experience brand is quite different to that of products that we wear or gadgets that we use, for we immerse ourselves in our environment, we incubate there. When the story of brand enters our living environment, it infiltrates our chrysalis experience. Our soft-wiring is shoe-horned into a concept that we live in, and while there, brand associations are triggering thoughts we live by. Much architecture triggers thoughts we live by, here it is an aspirational story that is guiding the synopsis.

With these, image and styling are calculated to match the narrative the owners aspire to, tapping their herding instincts and desire to belong. Musak often plays at party volume in the lobbies, and mood-lit corridors act as runways for the residents to strut their stuff. These are environments that seduce with their aspirationally-driven narrative, which dictates the potential bias of one's change. A tailored designer jacket does not have the same impact!

With our jacket, we are all a different size, shape and colour, and we team it with different garments as we change accessories through the seasons. We maintain something of our individual within the styling, whereas, with architecture shaped by brand, a collective of residents are living in, and looking at, the same architecture and associated story, day-in-day-out. The narrative and its emphasis feeding into one's drive to develop and evolve, influencing one's evolutionary path! Perhaps, as Churchill insightfully proposed of buildings, *'They regulate the course of our lives'*.

Lifestyle is not the surface fashion moment it appears to be, not when it shapes our environment. There, beyond the surrounding hypnosis of the narrative, it can also affect our gene expression.

There is the phrase: 'You can take the girl out of New York, but you can't take New York out of the girl'. Or Liverpool, London, Tokyo and on across the globe. More than just culturally, it is neurally so; all the way down to our gene expression and across the generations.

> In ways we have not imagined, our surroundings
> shape us even as we shape them.

□ □

Where the beaver builds a dam and the bird its nest, as we mark our environment, in synergy with our alchemy, our environment marks us.

Neutra said in *Life and Shape* – *'In future, architecture as I have looked at it also in the past, will depend on a deepened knowledge of nature, and of man's nature especially, however encroached on by his own patented artificialities.'*

Beyond the artificialities that Neutra insightfully referred to, if our environment is going to mark us at a profound level, let us first mark it with a synopsis that resonates with an authenticity we would delight in expressing. Let it nuture the liberated 'I' in me.

Joseph Campell said, *'The privilege of life is being who you are'.*

□ □

As regards the 'I' in me, our fingerprint is a clue for us to step outside the cult of the herd, for each of us is cut from a neural fabric that has billions of differentials. All woven from differing synaptic structures as our neurons self-organized at birth; producing our particular one in 7.5 billion. An individuality that we can overlook in our forgetfulness of the personal, the years of conditioning and our innate desire to belong.

□□

None of us can know for sure what this complex journey in life is ultimately about. Assuming the majesty of it all is woven as our experience for a reason... let us harness the benefits.

If we have the ability to proactively change the pathways of our brain, regenerate and reorganise, then let us do so. If an environment can 're-mind' us of the 'how' of that and influence us towards 'preferred personal change', day-in-day-out, then let us let it do so.

Then those paths that speak of the god or self within, may better resonate. We would be taking a lead from Emerson: 'Do not go where the path may lead – go instead where there is no path and leave a trail'. Our own.

Dear trail-blazers,

When considering design for a hospital setting, a school or a municipal building, aware of the previous information, we can develop a story and apply generic solutions, ergonomics and psychology of design. However, that route will not address the 'I' in me and its story. To source that, and frame it as a transformative design, we need an interactive experience, one that takes us beyond previously conditioned ideas.

For those who are interested in reaching beyond the familiar to uncover and explore a liberating story via design – please join me on the website below.

For those who were just curious, I hope you enjoyed the journey. For you, the clues compiled along the way may be enough to guide a more thoughtful approach, when you next choose change via design.

At the least, the question to ask when it comes to one's environment of choice is, 'where it touches us, is it taking us towards wellbeing or away from it?'

I wish you a smile in your mind.

Rosalyn

www.theroomthatchangesyourbrain.com

Victor Frankl,
suggested that
life has no meaning
save the one we give it.

In honour of his insight,
and with a nod to Neutra
and emerging science,
I suggest we let our room
mean something –
that our life may mean more.

RECOMMENDED READING LIST

Damasio, Antonio: *The feeling of what happens; Decarte's error*

Gazzaniga, Michael: *Cognitive neuroscience*

Gribben, John: *In search of Schroedinger's cat*

James & Jessel, Thomas: *Principles of neuroscience*

Jung, C G: *The red book*

Kandel, Erik: *In search of memory; Memory from mind to molecules*

Lakoff, George & Johnson, Mark: *The philosophy of the flesh*

Langer, Ellen: *Counterclockwise*

Ledoux, Joseph: *The emotional brain*

Libet, Benjamin: *Mind time*

Maslow, Abraham: *Motivation and personality. Theory of human motivation.*

Merleau-Ponty, Maurice: *Phenomenology of perception*

Michio, Kaku: *Parallel worlds; The physics of the impossible*

Neutra, Richard: *Life and shape*

Pert, Candace B: *Molecules of emotion*

Pinker, Steven: *How the mind works; The stuff of thought*

Ramachandran, V S: *A brief tour of human consciousness; The tell-tale brain*

Sacks, Oliver: *The man who mistook his wife for a hat*

Schwartz, Jeffrey: *The mind and the brain*

Smolin, Lee: *The trouble with physics*

Thompson, Eric: *Mind in life*

a zeitgeist is upon us